Specimen Sight-Reading Tests for Horn

Grades 1–5

ABRSM

GRADE 1

AB 2483

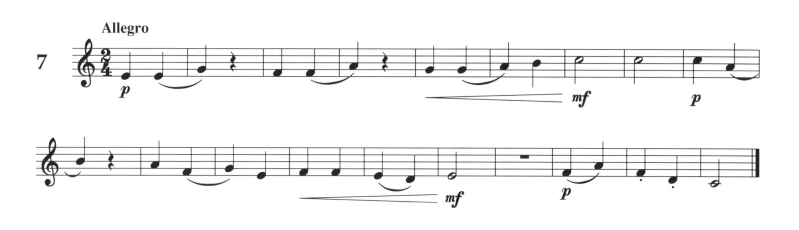

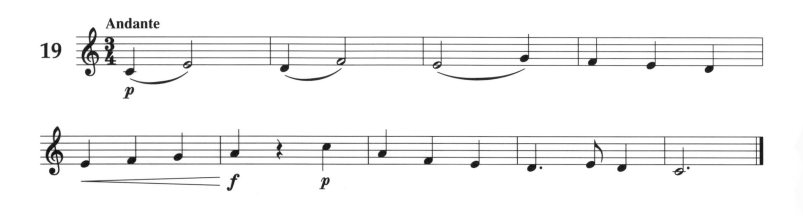

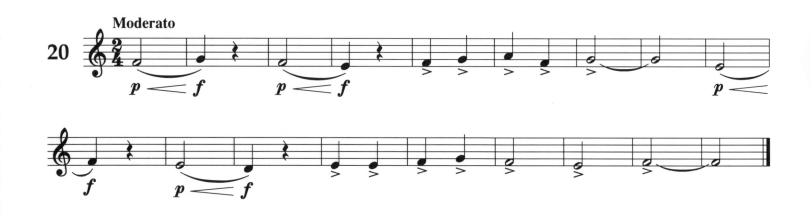

GRADE 2

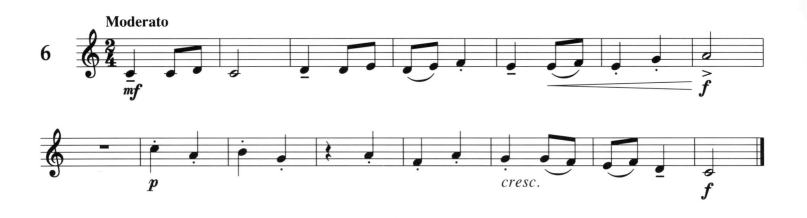

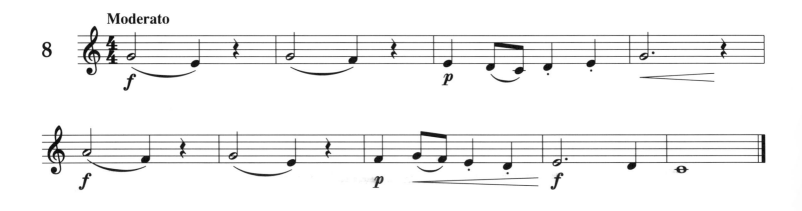

GRADE 3

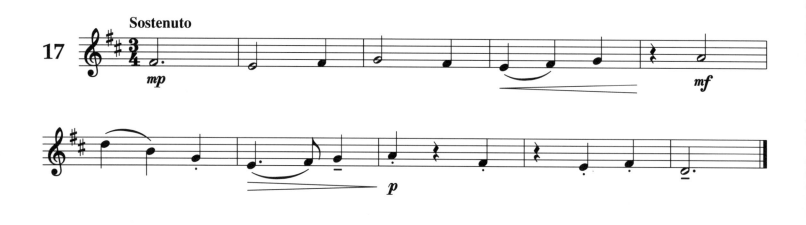

AB 2483

GRADE 4

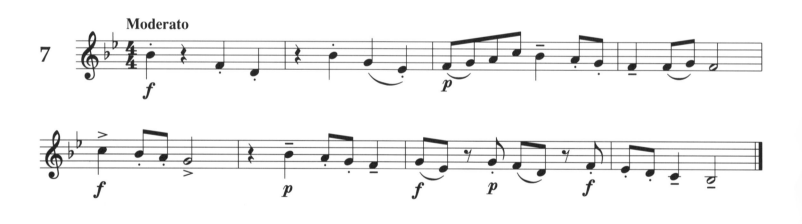

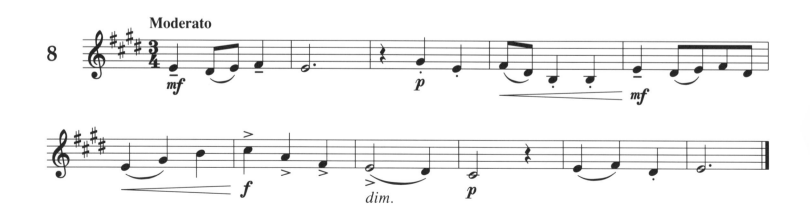

13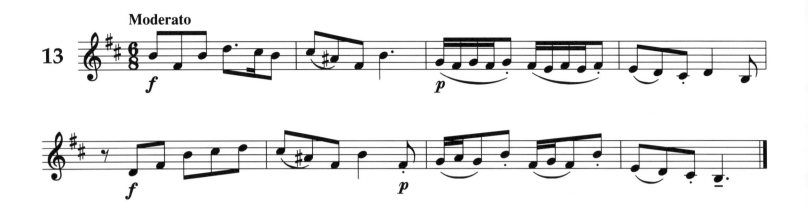

14

15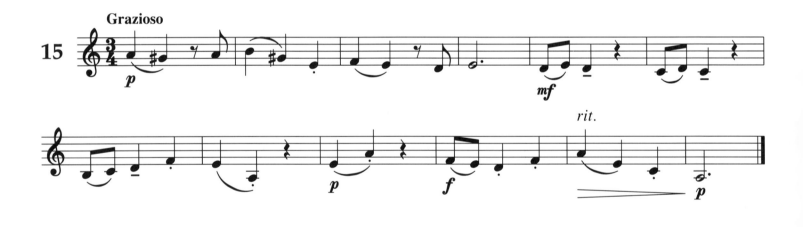

16

GRADE 5

13 Vivo

14 Risoluto

15 Ritmico

16 Moderato

AB 2483

Printed and bound in Great Britain by
Caligraving Limited Thetford Norfolk 3.11